ENDER'S GAME

CHARACTER GUIDE

By Mike Jay

SCHOLASTIC INC.

ISBN 978-0-545-61479-5

12 11 10 9 8 7 6 5 4 3 2 1   13 14 15 16 17 18/0

Printed in the U.S.A.
First printing, November 2013

CONTENTS

EARTH'S ONLY HOPE...

Fifty years after the invasion of Earth, an alien race is poised to attack again. The Formic fleet is more powerful than ever, and only one thing stands between humanity and certain destruction: an army of the planet's best and bravest.

An army of strategically brilliant minds trained on a single goal.

But an army is nothing without its commander. The International Fleet has searched far and wide for someone to lead Earth's forces to victory. Now the fate of humanity rests on the shoulders of one young man. He's spent his life playing military games, and he's never lost a single one.

But war is the ultimate game. Does he have what it takes to win?

"I've watched through his eyes, and I tell you . . . he's the one."
— Colonel Hyrum Graff

ENDER WIGGIN AND FAMILY

ANDREW "ENDER" WIGGIN

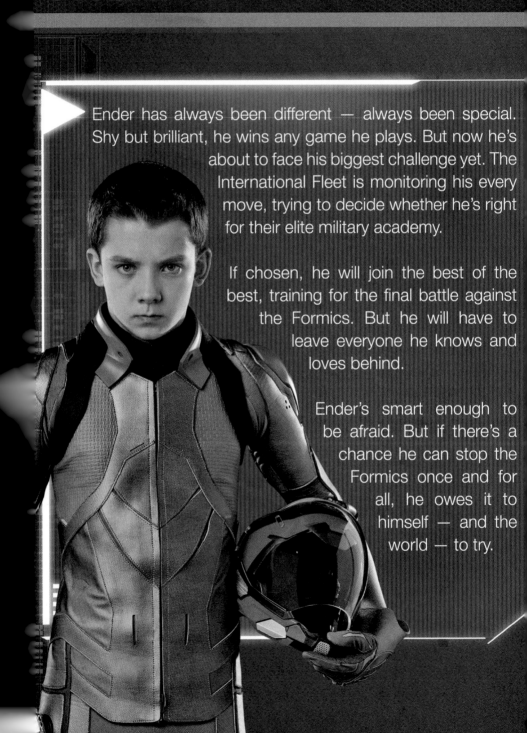

Ender has always been different — always been special. Shy but brilliant, he wins any game he plays. But now he's about to face his biggest challenge yet. The International Fleet is monitoring his every move, trying to decide whether he's right for their elite military academy.

If chosen, he will join the best of the best, training for the final battle against the Formics. But he will have to leave everyone he knows and loves behind.

Ender's smart enough to be afraid. But if there's a chance he can stop the Formics once and for all, he owes it to himself — and the world — to try.

LEARNING HOW TO WIN

Not everyone wants Ender to succeed. When Stilson, another student at his military school, loses to Ender one too many times, he decides to take his revenge. Ender tries being humble, he tries reason, he tries avoiding confrontation — but nothing works.

Stilton attacks, and even though he's older and bigger, Ender knocks him to the ground. Not because he wants to, because he *has* to. It's the strategic thing to do. It's the way to win not just this fight, but the next one.

That's when recruiters from the International Fleet decide he's the one they've been looking for. Ender Wiggin may be small in stature, but he's smart and intuitive — and he knows how to win.

PETER WIGGIN

Handsome, confident, and utterly ruthless, Ender's older brother, Peter, has never gotten over his rejection by the International Fleet. He can't forgive Ender for being the special one — so he does everything he can to make his brother's life miserable.

Ender's biggest fear is that he and Peter are the same. He's terrified he might have the same inclination toward violence as his older brother. But unlike Ender, Peter *enjoys* confrontation. He likes having power over those who are weaker than him — and as far as he's concerned, that's everyone.

Ender's older sister is the absolute opposite of Peter. Gentle, kind, and full of empathy, Valentine will do anything for the people she loves. And there's no one she loves as much as Ender.

Valentine and Ender have a special bond, one that connects them even when Ender is a world away, cut off from all communication. Valentine will always love him, and Ender knows that. When he's pushed to his breaking point, it's Valentine's love that brings him back from the brink.

If Peter teaches Ender about ruthlessness and gives him the will to win, Valentine gives him something even more important: a reason to fight.

THERESA AND JOHN WIGGIN

When John Wiggin was a boy, the Fleet brought him over from Poland to train for battle. But like so many promising young cadets, he washed out of the program. Instead of devoting his life to battling the Formics, he grew up on Earth, became a professor, and fell in love.

John and Theresa married, had two children, and then petitioned the government for permission to have a third. Ender has always believed this was because they wanted to increase their chances of getting a child into Battle School. But John and Theresa love Ender for who he is, not what he can do. When Colonel Graff finally comes to recruit him for Battle School, both John and Theresa are heartbroken.

"So this is Battle School. Every day, hours of training. And far more homework than we ever had on Earth. . . ."

— Ender Wiggin

MAKING IT TO BATTLE SCHOOL

Getting into Battle School is nearly impossible . . . but once you've gotten in, getting *to* Battle School is no piece of cake, either.

Battle School is hidden away on a station deep in space. You can only get there by space shuttle. Ender and the other new students have never been into space. They don't know what to expect. Hurtling through space means floating in zero gravity, and that's not for everyone.

When they dock at the space station's airlock, there's no one waiting to take their hands. There's just a loud-speaker, ordering them to follow the yellow lights that lead to their barracks.

It's their first clue: Nothing here is like home. This is Battle School, and from their first minute on deck, they've joined the war.

WELCOME TO BATTLE SCHOOL

Battle School is an elite academy where war is the ultimate game. The curriculum is tough: Nearly every minute of the day is spent in class, training, or in simulated battle. The cadets' minds, bodies, and spirits are pushed to the extreme.

Why must the training be so intense when the cadets are still so young? As the school's leader, Colonel Hyrum Graff, puts it, young minds are best at "complex data integration." Translation: Kids are better at solving problems quickly and creatively, coming up with strategies adults could never imagine. Grown-ups may run the school, but it's kids who will win the war.

Each recruit is assigned to a team that lives and trains together as an army. Communication with family back home is forbidden. The only thing that matters is doing well in school. And that means doing well in the Battle Room.

PRACTICE BATTLE

Battle School recruits spend much of their time in the Battle Room, engaged in an intense war game. Cadets are obsessed with practice battle — planning for it, training for it, playing it, and ranking themselves in it. The best players are the ones who get to move on to Command School. That's every cadet's dream.

Battles can take place at any time, without warning. Players float through the Battle Room with flash guns, trying to immobilize the other army. Everyone wears padded suits that freeze up when hit by a flash-gun fire. Each army also has a gate to guard — if you can get a player through the enemy's gate unharmed, it's an automatic win.

The mess hall has a giant scoreboard, where the army rankings are constantly updated. Your status in the game is the only status that matters. Great players are worshipped and admired, while weaker players are pitied and disdained.

THE BATTLE ROOM

The Battle Room has two circular gates, one on each side. This is how the armies enter the Battle Room. The gate must be protected from the enemy at all costs.

The Battle Room is zero-G, just like space. As part of the recruits' training, Colonel Graff configures steel "stars" in different formations for each battle. These stars drift across the emptiness, and players use them both for cover and maneuvering.

The most important thing for a player to remember is that in zero-G, playing well means letting go of real-world orientations like up and down. After all, there's no such thing as up and down in space.

This is Ender's first moment of genius at Battle School. Before any of the other launchies in his team, he figures out the only orientation that matters: "The

THE MIND GAME

The cadets may not realize it, but the Battle Game isn't the only game that matters.

Ender finds the Mind Game on his **desk-pad**. Ender plays as a mouse, facing off against a giant who offers him two goblets. Choose wisely, and he will be allowed to pass — or so the giant says. However, no matter which goblet Ender chooses, the mouse dies a horrible death.

Soon he figures out the trick of the game: The only way to win is to break the rules.

Little does Ender realize that the Mind Game is actually a diagnostic tool designed by Major Anderson. She and Colonel Graff monitor the game play to get glimpses of their students' frame of mind.

Is there too much pressure on Ender to succeed? Will he rise to the challenge, as Graff believes? Or will it prove too much for him, as Anderson fears? What will happen to the human race if she's right?

"A great responsibility rests upon each of you. . . ."

— Colonel Hyrum Graff

THE RECRUITS

JULIAN "BEAN" DELPHIKI, JR.

Bean may be the smallest cadet at Battle School, but he's got a big mouth and an even bigger brain. He grew up on the streets, which is where he earned his nickname. As the youngest of the street kids he ran with, people figured he "wasn't worth a bean."

But Bean's used to being underestimated, and he knows how to use it to his advantage. He excels at the Battle Game, and he sneak-attacks his way to victory.

Bean is one of the first to recognize Ender's greatness — and Ender, in turn, realizes that the little cadet could be a powerful ally. The two team up to take the Dragon Army straight to the top of the scoreboard. When Ender leaves Battle School to face his greatest challenge yet, Bean is beside him as his right-hand man.

"The enemy's gate is down . . . they're like a bug to be crushed under our feet"

BERNARD

When Ender first meets Bernard, he seems like a troublemaker. Bernard loves to pick on kids who are smaller than he is — in fact, he loves to pick on everyone.

But Ender sees something buried inside him (*deep* inside). He sees the potential for something better. Bernard has what it takes to be a good soldier, and even a good ally. He just needs to learn that making wisecracks isn't the way to lead.

He learns this lesson when other launchies switch their allegiance from Bernard to Ender. Bernard may be tough, but Ender is fair and loyal, and that shows an even greater strength.

Bernard always had what it takes to be a great soldier — but thanks to Ender, he discovers what it takes to be a great man.

"What am I doing here, Ender? You don't even like me."

Recruited from Persia at age fourteen, Alai gets off to a rocky start at Battle School. He pukes on the shuttle, making him a target for some of his fellow students.

Alai has dignity and an unbreakable spirit, and he refuses to be deterred from his goals. Ender sees his potential, and he stands up for Alai when Bernard teases him. In doing so, Ender wins himself an unshakeable ally — and a friend for life.

"Peace to you...."

BONZO MADRID

A Battle Room superstar, Bonzo uses fear and intimidation to lead his troops. What he lacks in size he makes up for in fierceness and intensity. Under his command, Salamander Army rules the top of the scoreboard. And Bonzo (pronounced "Bone-So") rules the school.

Bonzo has his army's obedience . . . but not their respect. When Ender shows up to challenge his supremacy, Bonzo can't handle it. He's terrified everyone will realize his strategies aren't solely responsible for Salamander's triumphs.

What starts as a rivalry quickly turns into an all-out vendetta. Blinded by jealousy, Bonzo will stop at nothing to destroy his nemesis. Ender tries to calm him, but Bonzo refuses to hear reason. When he attacks Ender, the fight will change both their lives forever.

"Don't you ever turn your back on me!"

One of the only girls at Battle School, Petra is a headstrong outsider who fights twice as hard to prove herself. She earns respect in the Battle Room with her exceptional skills as a sharpshooter.

When Ender joins Salamander Army, Petra is the only one to defy Bonzo and help train him. She gives Ender one-on-one sessions in their free time, teaching him target shooting, hand-to-hand combat, and advanced battle moves. Ender becomes Petra's first real friend, and Petra becomes a trusted ally that Ender can't do without.

"The enemy is deadly, but Petra is steady."

DINK MEEKER

Rank: Rat Army Soldier

A natural-born talent, Dink Meeker lets his actions on the battlefield speak louder than words. Dink's strategies are the key to his army's victories, but he prefers to let his commander take the credit. While other students are desperate to rise through the ranks, Dink has already turned down two promotions. He thinks power makes people crazy, and he's happy just the way he is.

Dink takes Ender under his wing early on. Because he doesn't care about getting ahead, he's got no reason to be jealous. He recognizes Ender as a genius and tries to help him.

Dink reminds Ender that *winning* at Battle School isn't everything. He loves the game, but he never forgets it's only a game. There are more important things in life.

"I love the game ... —but just remember, it's only a game."

FLY MOLO

Rank: Salamander Army Soldier

One of the top fighters in Bonzo's Salamander Army, Fly Molo has dedicated his life to becoming a world-class International Fleet commander. Born in the Philippines, he dreams of growing up in the stars.

When Ender gets to lead his own army, Fly is a crucial player. He uses his superior intelligence to find his enemies' weakness and make them pay.

"Asp is gonna win, boss. . . ."

ENDER'S BATTLE WISDOM

Ender Wiggin has proved himself to be one of the best strategic thinkers in the galaxy. Here's how he does it:

"The enemy's gate is down."

"You have to use what's around you."

"Knocking him down was the first fight. I wanted to win all the next ones, too."

"If anyone has an idea they think is better than mine, I wanna hear it."

"In a battle with the Formics, there will be no rules."

"I've won because I've always understood how the enemy thinks."

"I can't win if I never take any risks."

"It's impossible to truly understand someone and not to love them the way they love themselves. But in that moment . . . I destroy them."

THE ARMIES

Every cadet at Battle School is assigned an army. Whether you're on Manticore, Asp, Rat, Salamander, Leopard, or Dragon, you've got one mission: to serve your commander and strive for victory.

Dragon Army

Salamander Army

Rat Army

Snake Army

SALAMANDER ARMY

When Ender arrives at Battle School, there's no question which army's on top. Under Bonzo's leadership, Salamander Army has won twenty out of its last twenty-one battles.

Hotheaded as always, Bonzo has no use for Ender — he orders Ender not to participate in battle, even though many of the other Salamander players can see that the new recruit knows his stuff. But Ender knows that sometimes rules have to be broken. During his very first battle he ends up rescuing some fellow soldiers and helping them win.

It's not long before Ender ends up head of Dragon Army. And soon Dragon and Salamander face off in a major showdown....

Salamander Army Cheer: *Salamander is number one! No one like us under the sun!*

Salamander superstars: Petra Arkanian, Dink Meeker, Fly Molo

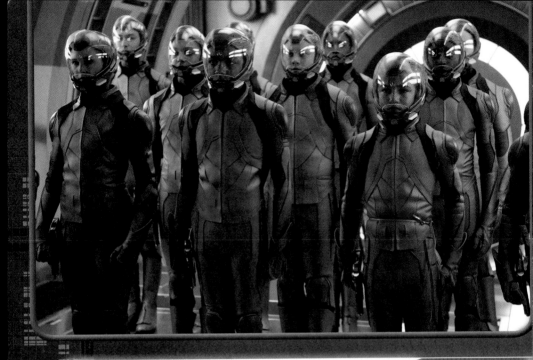

DRAGON ARMY

Dragon Army is the ultimate underdog. No Dragon Army has ever won a single battle, so four years ago, the name was discontinued. But Colonel Graff brings the unlucky army back to life — and he puts Ender in charge.

Now the youngest, most inexperienced commander at Battle School will lead a team of misfits to victory. Under Ender's unique command, every player gets a say — and every idea, no matter how crazy, gets a hearing. Thanks to creative thinking and sheer determination, Dragon Army rockets to the top of the scoreboard.

Not everyone's happy about this. But it doesn't matter, because Dragon Army lets no one stand in their way. They stay on top, no matter what the other armies — and Colonel Graff — throw at them. Overcoming one impossible challenge after the next, Dragon Army proves it's truly the best of the best.

Dragon Army hotshots:
Alai, Petra Arkanian,
Bernard, Bean Delphiki,

COMMAND

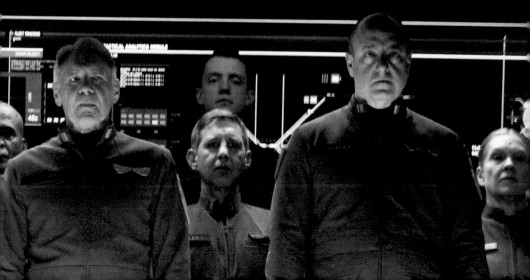

"The Formics could have wiped us out. You know, the only thing that saved us was having a brilliant commander."

— Colonel Hyrum Graff

As a commander in the International Fleet, Colonel Graff is a man burdened by great responsibility. He knows his decisions could mean the salvation of humanity — or its destruction. The burden weighs on him: You can see it in every line and crease on his face. But you can also see that he's up to the challenge. He's a man driven by duty — the battle against the Formics is his life.

It's Graff who must forge the young Battle School recruits into the heroes of tomorrow, and it's Graff who sees the hero in Ender before Ender sees it in himself. He cares deeply about the young soldier, but knows he must push Ender to his limits — and beyond — if Ender's going to reach his potential. Graff will do *anything* to win. And that's what weighs heaviest on his overburdened shoulders: He knows that sometimes war demands sacrifice. Sometimes victory comes at a price.

"The morality of what we are doing is a luxury we can debate when this war is over."

MAJOR
GWEN ANDERSON

A military psychologist for the International Fleet, Major Anderson specializes in the molding of children into soldiers. She works closely with her commanding officer, Colonel Graff, advising him on the students' problems and weaknesses. She often serves as Graff's conscience, urging him to remember the cadets are still children, and warning him when he pushes too far.

Major Anderson monitors the Mind Games. She knows better than anyone else how close Ender is to the edge, but Graff doesn't want to listen to her warnings. She has to decide how much to question his actions. Her job is to protect Ender — and the soul of Battle School itself — but is that worth ruining her career?

"Not every battle can be won."

ADMIRAL JAWARHALAL CHAMRAJNAGAR

The International Fleet is an armada of galactic warships sworn to protect humanity. As Strategos of the Fleet, Admiral Chamrajnagar is ultimately responsible for the fate of the human race. With the Formics rebuilding their fleet, the Admiral knows another attack is imminent — but until he has a commander worthy of leading the Fleet into battle, there's nothing to be done but wait.

Colonel Graff has promised him that this time, he's found someone special. Admiral Chamrajnagar has no choice but to trust him. The admiral may be the most powerful man alive, but his future, like everyone else's, now rests in the hands of a child.

So he reads Graff's reports. And he waits . . . and hopes.

"Our survival demands that we focus *all* our resources on the destruction of the enemy."

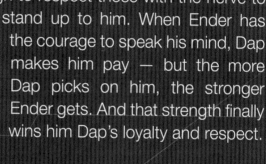

SERGEANT JAMES DAP

A smart-mouthed drill sergeant charged with turning a group of clueless launchies into hardened Battle School cadets, Sergeant Dap comes on strong. His strategy? Terrify the cadets into obeying his every word. (It works.)

Dap has a wicked sense of humor, and he's confident and capable enough to respect those with the nerve to stand up to him. When Ender has the courage to speak his mind, Dap makes him pay — but the more Dap picks on him, the stronger Ender gets. And that strength finally wins him Dap's loyalty and respect.

As Ender rises through the ranks, Dap stays by his side. When Ender finally takes command, Dap readily salutes him. More than anyone, Dap knows that he's earned it.

"If you want a shoulder to cry on, use a pillow."

COMMAND SCHOOL

Only the best of the best make it into Battle School . . . and from there, only the very *best* get promoted to the next level: Command School. Very few kids at Battle School will make the cut — and even those who do have no idea what to expect.

Everything about Command School is top secret, from its curriculum to its location. When Ender is selected, all he knows is that Command School is where he'll receive his final training. He'll learn from the greatest living military minds, and prove whether or not he's the one they've been looking for, the great hope of defeating the Formics.

If Ender succeeds, the Strategos will make him the commander of the entire Fleet. If he fails, then all is lost.

Failure is not an option.

PLANET EROS

When Ender is sent to Command School, he finally discovers the truth about its secret location: The International Fleet command is headquartered on Planet Eros, a rocky planet deep in interstellar space.

A planet that once belonged to the Formics.

Planet Eros was once the forward staging post for the Formics' invasion of Earth. Now the International Fleet is using it for the same purpose.

After an impossibly long trip in an interstellar cargo transporter, Ender wakes from his **cryo-bed** to discover a rugged landscape dotted with strange alien structures. Cavern-like rooms have been refitted as command centers; metal walkways are bolted into walls carved with alien designs. Human furniture looks alien in the strange environment. Even the planet's atmosphere is inhospitable to humanity.

The International Fleet is massed at the Formic home planet, waiting for attack orders. Planet Eros is close enough that Command can communicate with the ships by **Ansible** — all they need is a commander sharp enough to give the right orders.

And everyone's hoping that will be Ender.

"From now on, you are always about to lose."
—Mazer Rackham

THE FORMICS

Ever since the first invasion, humankind has been busy studying these strange creatures, trying to learn more about the enemy. But for all we have learned about the Formics, they still remain thoroughly alien.

Antlike creatures with compound eyes, the Formics have no vocal cords, so it is believed they have no way of speaking. Though they may have found a way to communicate with one another, they've revealed no ability or inclination to speak to humans. Their only form of communication has been attack.

Their forces are massed around the Formic home world. The planet's high surface temperature means they can only be aboveground for a few hours a day. Most of their lives are spent in tunnels underground. Water is scarce, and as the population grows, demand will soon exceed supply. The Formics must find another planet to colonize, or go extinct.

This is why they need Earth — and why the International Fleet intends to stop them. It's either us or them.

RACKHAM

THE FIRST FORMIC INVASION

Fifty years ago, humanity knew nothing of alien life. Then, without warning, the Formics came to our solar system — and attacked. Across Earth, cities burned. Millions died. Survivors fled through the ruins, running for their lives as the Formics tried to eradicate everyone.

Humans threw everything they had at the Formics, but the combined military might of every country on Earth still wasn't enough. It took the genius and bravery of one man, Mazer Rackham, to save the human race from extinction.

In that final, decisive battle, Mazer Rackham sacrificed his ship in a desperate charge on a Formic mothership. Somehow, he destroyed the entire fleet. The details of the battle are classified top secret.

Now another war is imminent. Without another Mazer Rackham, it will be lost.

Fifty years ago, Mazer Rackham was just another International Fleet pilot. He was fearless but unremarkable — until he launched the attack that won the war. Everyone on Earth believes he made the ultimate sacrifice, that he surrendered his life in a blaze of glory. But humanity's greatest hero has lived a long, lonely life in isolation in the far reaches of the galaxy.

Now the Fleet needs its savior once again.

Descended from a warrior race, Mazer Rackham lost his father to the First Formic War. He has covered his face in Maori tattoos — *Ta Moko* — as a way to stay connected to his father and their shared past. To speak for the dead.

Rackham knows more about the enemy than anyone alive, and that understanding just might be the key to defeating the Formics once and for all. But only if Ender can rise to the challenge.

With limited wisdom and zero mercy, Mazer becomes Ender's mentor. "There is no teacher but the enemy," he tells Ender. He becomes both the greatest enemy and the greatest ally Ender has ever known.

With his help, Ender will finally become the hero he was

GLOSSARY

Ansible – a faster-than-light communication device that allows military command to communicate instantaneously with the Fleet, even over interstellar distances

bug – the loser in any Battle School launch group, the weakest link (also slang for Formics)

cryo-bed – a cryogenic chamber on interstellar spaceships; passengers cryogenically frozen to withstand the voyage, and then defrosted on the other end

desk-pad – a portable, holographic computing device used for homework, communication, and recreation

formation – a strategic array of 'toons across the Battle Room in pre-arranged positions

Hegemon – the political ruler of Earth

hook – the remote control device used to unfreeze Battle Game flash suits after a battle

IF – abbreviation for International Fleet, the armada of ships protecting Earth from Formic invasion

launchies – slang for new arrivals to Battle School

M.D. 500 – the Molecular Detachment Device, aka "the little Doctor" — a powerful weapon that shatters molecular bonds until nothing is left, equivalent to seventy billion tons of pure destruction

monitor – a small machine implanted into the necks of children who might be candidates for Battle School; it allows the International Fleet to see and hear everything they do

Strategos – the leader of the International Fleet, commander ultimately responsible for defense of Earth